Adjudicator's Contract

This contract should be used for the appointment of an Adjudicator to decide disputes under the NEC family of contracts. It may also be used for the appointment of an Adjudicator under other forms of contract

An NEC document

June 2005

OGC endorsement of NEC3

OGC advises public sector procurers that the form of contract used has to be selected according to the objectives of the project, aiming to satisfy the *Achieving Excellence in Construction* (AEC) principles.

This edition of the NEC (NEC3) complies fully with the AEC principles. OGC recommends the use of NEC3 by public sector construction procurers on their construction projects.

Office of Government Commerce

NEC is a division of Thomas Telford Ltd, which is a wholly owned subsidiary of the Institution of Civil Engineers (ICE), the owner and developer of the NEC.

The NEC is a family of standard contracts, each of which has these characteristics:

- Its use stimulates good management of the relationship between the two parties to the contract and, hence, of the work included in the contract.
- It can be used in a wide variety of commercial situations, for a wide variety of types of work and in any location.
- It is a clear and simple document – using language and a structure which are straightforward and easily understood.

NEC3 Adjudicator's Contract is one of the NEC family and is consistent with all other NEC3 documents. Also available are the Guidance Notes and Flow Charts.

ISBN (complete box set) 0 7277 3382 6
ISBN (this document) 0 7277 3374 5
ISBN (Adjudicator's Contract Guidance Notes and Flow Charts) 0 7277 3375 3

First edition 1994
Second edition 1998
Third edition June 2005

Cover photo, Golden Jubilee Bridge, courtesy of City of Westminster

9 8 7 6 5 4 3 2 1

British Library Cataloguing in Publication Data for this publication is available from the British Library.

Typeset by Academic + Technical, Bristol

Printed and bound in Great Britain by Bell & Bain Limited, Glasgow, UK

CONTENTS

ACKNOWLEDGEMENTS

The first edition of the Adjudicator's Contract was drafted by Peter Higgins working on behalf of the Institution of Civil Engineers with the assistance of Frank Griffiths of the Chartered Institute of Purchasing and Supply and Michael Coleman of the Association of Project Managers. Dr Martin Barnes of Coopers and Lybrand advised on the co-ordination of the contract with the NEC.

The second edition of the NEC Adjudicator's Contract was produced by the Institution of Civil Engineers through its NEC Panel and was mainly drafted by Bill Weddell, with the assistance of Peter Higgins and Tom Nicholson, as members of NEC Panel with advice from Professor Phillip Capper then of Masons Solicitors. The Flow Charts were produced by John Perry, Ross Hayes and colleagues at the University of Birmingham.

The third edition of the NEC Adjudicator's Contract was mainly drafted by Peter Higgins with the assistance of members of the NEC Panel. The Flow Charts were produced by Robert Gerrard and Ross Hayes with assistance from Tom Nicholson.

The original NEC was designed and drafted by Dr Martin Barnes then of Coopers and Lybrand with the assistance of Professor J. G. Perry then of the University of Birmingham, T. W. Weddell, then of Travers Morgan Management, T. H. Nicholson, Consultant to the Institution of Civil Engineers, A. Norman, then of the University of Manchester Institute of Science and Technology, and P. A. Baird, then Corporate Contracts Consultant, Eskom, South Africa.

The members of the NEC Panel are:

P. Higgins, BSc, CEng, FICE, FCIArb (Chairman)
P. A. Baird, BSc, CEng, FICE, M(SA)ICE, MAPM
M. Barnes, BSc(Eng), PhD, FREng, FICE, FCIOB, CCMI, ACIArb, MBCS, FInstCES, FAPM
A. J. Bates, FRICS, MInstCES
A. J. M. Blackler, BA, LLB(Cantab), MCIArb
P. T. Cousins, BEng(Tech), DipArb, CEng, MICE, MCIArb, MCMI
L. T. Eames, BSc, FRICS, FCIOB
F. Forward, BA(Hons), DipArch, MSc(Const Law), RIBA, FCIArb
Professor J. G. Perry, MEng, PhD, CEng, FICE, MAPM
N. C. Shaw, FCIPS, CEng, MIMechE
T. W. Weddell, BSc, CEng, DIC, FICE, FIStructE, ACIArb

NEC Consultant:

R. A. Gerrard, BSc(Hons), MRICS, FCIArb, FInstCES

Secretariat:

A. Cole, LLB, LLM, BL
J. M. Hawkins, BA(Hons), MSc
F. N. Vernon (Technical Adviser), BSc, CEng, MICE

nec3 Adjudicator's Contract

FORM OF AGREEMENT

This Agreement is made on the . . . . day of . . . . between

- . . . . (name of company/organisation)

  of . . . .

  . . . .

  . . . . (address) and

- . . . . (name of company/organisation)

  of . . . .

  . . . .

  . . . . (address)

(the Parties) and

- . . . . (name)

  of . . . .

  . . . .

  . . . . (address)

(the Adjudicator).

1. The Parties appoint the Adjudicator in accordance with the conditions of contract and Contract Data attached to this Agreement.

2. The Adjudicator accepts this appointment and undertakes to carry out the Adjudicator's duties as described in the conditions of contract.

Signed jointly on behalf of the Parties by

. . . . (signature)

Name . . . .

Position . . . .

on behalf of . . . .

and

. . . . (signature)

Name . . . .

Position . . . .

on behalf of . . . .

and signed by the Adjudicator

. . . . (signature)

form of agreement

conditions of contract

contract data

nec 3 Adjudicator's Contract

CONDITIONS OF CONTRACT

1 General

Actions	1.1	The Parties and the Adjudicator shall act as stated in this contract and in the *contract between the Parties.* The Adjudicator shall act impartially.
	1.2	The Adjudicator notifies the Parties as soon as he becomes aware of any matter which may present him with a conflict of interest.
Identified and defined terms	1.3	In these conditions of contract, the Adjudicator and the Parties are those identified in the Form of Agreement. Terms identified in the Contract Data are in italics and defined terms have capital initials.
	1.4	Expenses are the cost of

* printing, reproduction and purchase of documents, drawings, maps, records and photographs,
* telegrams, telex, faxes and telephone calls,
* postage and delivery charges,
* travelling, hotel and similar expenses,
* room charges and
* charges by others for help in an adjudication

incurred by the Adjudicator for an adjudication.

Interpretation and the law	1.5	In this contract, except where the context shows otherwise, words in the singular also mean in the plural and the other way round and words in the masculine also mean in the feminine and neuter.
	1.6	This contract is governed by the *law of the contract.*
	1.7	If a conflict arises between this contract and the *contract between the Parties* then this contract prevails.
	1.8	If as a result of the *contract between the Parties* another party has become a party to a dispute which is to be decided by the Adjudicator, references to Parties in this contract are interpreted as including the other party.
Communications	1.9	Each communication which this contract requires is in a form which can be read, copied and recorded. Writing is in the *language of this contract.*
	1.10	A communication has effect when it is received at the last address notified by the recipient for receiving communications or, if none is notified, at the address of the recipient stated in the Form of Agreement.

2 Adjudication

2.1 The Adjudicator does not decide any dispute that is the same or substantially the same as one that he or his predecessor has previously decided.

2.2 The Adjudicator decides a dispute referred to him under the *contract between the Parties.* He makes his decision and notifies the Parties of it in accordance with the *contract between the Parties.*

2.3 After notifying the Parties of his intention, the Adjudicator may obtain from others help that he considers necessary in reaching his decision. Before making his decision, the Adjudicator provides the Parties with a copy of any information or advice from others and invites their comments on it.

2.4 The Parties co-operate with the Adjudicator and comply with any request or direction he makes in relation to the dispute.

2.5 The Parties and the Adjudicator keep the Adjudicator's decision and information provided for an adjudication as confidential to those who have a proper interest in them.

2.6 After a decision has been made, the Adjudicator keeps documents provided to him by the Parties for the *period of retention.*

3 Payment

Advanced payment 3.1 Each time a dispute is referred to the Adjudicator, the Party referring the dispute makes an advanced payment to him of the amount stated in the Contract Data. The advanced payment is made within one week of the date when the dispute is referred.

Assessing the amount due 3.2 The Adjudicator assesses the amount due and submits an invoice to each Party for that Party's share of the amount due. Unless otherwise agreed, the Parties pay the Adjudicator the amount due in equal shares.

3.3 The Adjudicator submits invoices after each decision on a dispute has been notified to the Parties and after termination.

3.4 The amount due is

- the Adjudicator's *fee* multiplied by the total of the time spent on an adjudication and the time spent travelling, plus
- the Expenses, less
- the amount of the advanced payment and other previous payments.

Any tax which the law requires the Parties to pay to the Adjudicator is included in the invoice.

Payment of the amount due 3.5 The Parties pay the amount due within three weeks of receiving the Adjudicator's invoice or, if a different period is stated in the Contract Data, within the period stated.

3.6 Payments are in the *currency of this contract* unless otherwise stated in this contract.

form of agreement

conditions of contract

contract data

3.7 If a payment is late, interest is paid on the late payment. Interest is assessed from the date by which the late payment should have been made until the date when the late payment is made. Interest is calculated on a daily basis at the *interest rate* and is compounded annually.

3.8 If one of the Parties fails to pay, the other Party pays the Adjudicator the amount due with interest. The defaulting Party repays to the other Party the amount paid to the Adjudicator together with interest.

4 Termination

4.1 The Parties may, by agreement, terminate the appointment of the Adjudicator for any reason. They notify the Adjudicator of the termination.

4.2 The Adjudicator may, by notifying the Parties, terminate his appointment if

- he considers that he cannot act because of a conflict of interest,
- he is unable to decide a dispute,
- an advance payment has not been made or
- he has not been paid an amount due within five weeks of the date by which payment should have been made.

4.3 Unless he has terminated his appointment or his appointment has been terminated by the Parties, the Adjudicator's appointment terminates on the date stated in the Contract Data.

CONTRACT DATA

Statements given in all contracts

- The *contract between the Parties* is . . . .
- The *period of retention* is . . . . weeks.
- The *law of the contract* is the law of . . . .
- The *language of this contract* is . . . .
- The amount of the advanced payment is . . . .
- The Adjudicator's *fee* is . . . . per hour.
- The *interest rate* is . . . . % per annum above
  . . . .
- The *currency of this contract* is . . . .
- The Adjudicator's appointment terminates on . . . .

Optional statements

If the period for payment of invoices is not three weeks

- The period for payment of invoices is . . . . weeks.

If *additional conditions of contract* are required

- The *additional conditions of contract* are

  . . . .
  . . . .
  . . . .
  . . . .

form of agreement

conditions of contract

contract data

nec 3 Adjudicator's Contract

Index by clause numbers (main clause heads indicated by bold numbers).
Terms in *italics* are identified in the Contract Data, and defined terms have capital initial letters.

A KEY TO TYNWALD

AN INTRODUCTION TO THE ISLE OF MAN

CH00684154

SARA GOODWINS

HOOFPRINT SERIES 8

Loaghtan Books
Caardee, Dreemskerry Hill
Maughold
Isle of Man
IM7 1BE

Published by Loaghtan Books

First published: March 2022

Typesetting and origination by:
Loaghtan Books

Printed and bound by:
Page Bros Print

Website: www.loaghtanbooks.com

ISBN: 978-1-908060-34-1

For Mary Lowe
who knows far more about politics than I do

Front cover: Tynwald Hill and the processional way to St John's Church *(Photograph © Jon Wornham)*

Rear cover: The Court of Tynwald from the dais where LegCo sits. Note the bust of Charles Kerruish observing procedings through the open door.

Title page: Stephen Rodan (left), President of Tynwald 2016-21, Juan Watterson, Speaker of the House of Keys 2016 to the time of writing, both in their finery on the processional way on Tynwald Day 2021.

Contents page: Detail from the President of Tynwald's robe. The yoke carries the Mustering Cross or *Crosh Vusta,* an ancient device carried around the parishes to summon the Manx to defend their island. It was reputedly last used in 1651 by Illiam Dhone. *(Photograph © Tynwald)*

Hoofprint series
A De-tailed Account of Manx Cats
Things to do with Vikings
Three Legs Good; the story of the Manx triskelion
Mann with Altitude
Two Fish for the Summit; life and work on the Manx mountain
A Manx A-B-C-Dery; an Alphabetical Tour of the Isle of Man
Cross Purposes; an introduction to mediaeval Manx crosses
A Key to Tynwald

CONTENTS

ACKNOWLEDGEMENTS

The author is indebted to several organisations and individuals who gave up their time to provide help, information and/or photographic material. They include, individuals: Ruth Donnelly, Susanne Eriksson, Alison Haley, Odd Harald Kvammen, Victoria Linblom, Roger Phillips, Margrét Sveinbjörnsdóttir, Louise Trimble, Lisbet Elkjær Vinther, Jon Wornham, Steven Wright; and organisations: Ålands Lagting, Information and Documentation Department of the Norwegian Storting, Information Office of the Danish Parliament, Information Service Tynwald, Secretariat of Althingi Parliament of Iceland.

Always of course I am grateful for the support and photographic expertise of my husband, George Hobbs.

Thank you all for your help and assistance; any mistakes are entirely mine.

CHAPTER 1

HISTORY OF TYNWALD

The history of Tynwald goes back more than a thousand years and has its origins hundreds of miles away from the Isle of Man. As far as we can gather, the whole idea of Tynwald arose out of a need to ensure fairness in a market place.

The word 'Tynwald'

Communities in Scandinavia lived in small groups isolated by forest and fjord. They met most frequently to trade goods, livestock, gossip and, occasionally, blows. To ensure things didn't get out of hand the most important men in the area got together to lay down some basic rules: don't cheat, don't steal, don't run off with someone else's girl/wife/mother and don't kill each other. All this happened probably around the sixth century.

> **DID YOU KNOW?**
>
> The letter Þ is pronounced 'th' as in 'worth'. Over the years Þ lost its top and began to look like the letter Y. This is why we occasionally have 'ye' for 'the'.

Over time such meetings became more formalised and were called a *þing* or Thing. At a Thing the free men wrangled over issues affecting their community and amended or added to local laws. What worked for small disputes worked for larger ones too. For issues which affected several communities, the areas' most influential men represented their neighbours (who came to watch and ensure fair play) at a joint meeting which they called an *Alþing* or All-thing. Sometimes the region covered by a Thing could form what might be called a petty kingdom: an area ruled by a single important chief. Even then, however, Things were instrumental in stopping squabbles within the fiefdom and keeping the peace with near neighbours.

To start with Things were held in any spacious area, but as they got bigger they needed more room, so a special area was often set aside for them. The Thing field was called *þing-völlr*, which over time became *Tinvaal* in Manx and Tynwald in English. As the *þing-völlr* was selected as being the most suitable for a large public meeting, it tended to be reused every time a Thing was held. Sometimes stone foundations were built for tents pitched on site, and such pitches would become temporary camp sites year after year.

Midsummer was a time for celebrating the year's light, warmth and fertility. Just as today families and friends like to meet for the occasional party, so then the clans wanted to get together, and it was much easier to do so in daylight. It therefore saved a lot of travelling if a Thing was held at the same time. On the Isle of Man Tynwald Day is still held on 5 July, Old Midsummer's Day.

> **DID YOU KNOW?**
>
> The idea of a Thing, with its political overtones, has also come into English in a modified form in the word 'hustings', where candidates for election address those who may (or may not!) choose to vote for them.

The Norwegian model

Things had been the mainstay of Nordic laws and government for hundreds of years when Vikings invaded the Isle of Man at the beginning of the ninth century. The Vikings who invaded Mann came mostly from what is now Norway, so the early Things on Mann were probably arranged like Norwegian Things of the same time; the Norsemen would have brought their customs with them. King Harald I of Norway also known as Harald Hárfagri or Harald Fairhair ('with the beautiful hair'), whose long reign lasted from 872 to 930, seems particularly to have recognised the stability which Things brought to his kingdom. In Norway the *Gulaþing* ('the Thing at Gulen') was the oldest and largest assembly, convened from around 900, partly to determine things like taxation, road building and war, and partly to judge and pass sentence on misdeeds. Local Things would probably have been established on Mann, therefore, almost as soon as the Vikings themselves arrived.

Only the Nordic sagas remain to hint how the early national Things were organised but it seems likely that the senior men or chiefs of each Thing area were expected to be there, together with two advisors. Chiefs might also insist that their supporters accompany them. While supporters had no legal influence, their sheer numbers – and ability to heckle – could be intimidating.

First Deemster Andrew Corlett promulgating the laws from Tynwald Hill. The 2020 Covid pandemic kept the hill empty of all personnel not directly involved in the ceremony

> ### DID YOU KNOW?
>
> The *Gulaþing* served as a model for the establishment of the legislative assemblies of Iceland and the Faroe Islands (see pages 30-1) and still exists as a court of appeal in Bergen, Norway.

Free citizens could also choose to attend either to bring suit or just to watch and see what was being decided for their area. A 'free man' seems to be defined as one who was not a slave, had a settled home, owned his own horse and was older than twelve. Women were allowed to be present, but were not allowed to debate. Interestingly it seems possible that those free men who chose not to attend the national Thing were expected to subsidise the expenses of those who did.

The site chosen for the national Thing, the *þing-völlr*, would ideally have had a raised area on which the representatives would sit, and possibly some sort of hill or rocky cliff behind the raised area (see page 30) to provide a natural sounding board to reflect voices – no microphones! Before the national Thing got down to business the site was blessed and a truce agreed. Weapons were either laid aside or vows taken not to draw or use them. It seems possible that the leaders sat in a circle with one advisor in front of them and one behind, so the whole formed three circles with everyone else watching.

The Thing was roughly divided into three parts. Firstly the existing laws were recited to all listening by the lawspeaker (*lagmann*), hence the need for natural amplification if at all possible. Before the time when laws were written down, the legal system relied on the memory of the lawspeakers to record the laws and rulings. In Iceland the lawspeaker recited a third of the laws at each Thing, so that it took three years to hear them all. Icelandic Things were based, at least at first, on Norwegian Things so such might also have been the case in Norway and the Isle of Man. The lawspeaker was a well-respected judge and it's possible that he also acted as the chairman of the Thing; he was certainly the only man who was paid.

The second part of the national Thing was the making of new laws which required a lot of wrangling and debate about what could be considered fair to individuals yet also in the best interest of the community. Finally, law suits and grievances were judged at the Thing, sometimes in what might now be called break-out groups: small courts would be convened for relatively minor offences in order to get through the legal business quickly. Serious matters would be judged by the senior men of the entire national Thing. Individuals and witnesses would state publically what the problem was, and the leaders would decide the rights of the case. The decision didn't have to be unanimous, but a majority vote would need at least three quarters (the proportions varied slightly over time) of the senior men to agree. Regulations were complicated in order to ensure that no-one was in doubt about the fairness of the decision.

While the serious legal concerns of the Thing were being transacted, trading and games would take place in different parts of the field. The Thing ended with the formal taking up of weapons, called the *vápnatak*; the term comes into English as wapentake.

DID YOU KNOW?

The leader of the House of Keys was called Chairman until 1758 when George Moore on his appointment as chairman preferred instead the title of Speaker in emulation of his counterpoint in Westminster.

The first Tynwald on Mann

In 1979 the Isle of Man celebrated 1,000 years of Tynwald, which suggests that the national Thing was established by 979. The first permanent Viking base on the Isle of Man is thought to have been established by about 835 and local Things would have been started almost at once, so establishing regular national Things by 979 is easily possible.

Site of Tynwald held at Killabane 1428. St Luke's church is just visible in the distance

It was often convenient to hold Tynwald in the same venue, but that wasn't necessarily the case. In 1422, for example, Tynwald was held 'upon the hill of Reneurling', which is thought to be near Barregarrow, south of Kirk Michael. Apart from the current Tynwald venue at St John's, two other Tynwald sites have been identified. One is near West Baldwin reservoir north of St Luke's church, and the other is at Cronk Urleigh upstream from Glen Wyllin on a small hill to the east of the current A3.

By this time, as well as a low hill on which the leaders of the assembly met, there was also

Site of Tynwald held until 1422 at Cronk Urleigh. Please note: the hill is on private land and there is no public access

a separate area for the courts to meet in, which doubled as a place of worship. The two were linked by a processional way, as is still the case at St John's: St Luke's was probably used at West Baldwin. Traditionally the low hill included a handful of earth brought by each representative from their local Thing area, so that all the representatives could think of the themselves as being on homeground and, more importantly, be governed by laws of hospitality. Even among the battle-loving Vikings it was considered rude to exchange fisticuffs with their guests.

The first records of Tynwald

We have no written records of the first Tynwalds on Mann and probably none was kept: the existence of the lawspeaker indicates that history was remembered rather than written down. One of the earliest written records to survive of the ceremony dates from 1417 and was written on the command of Sir John Stanley, the first of the family to rule the Isle of Man. The language is archaic but the ceremony described is recognisably the same as the one we celebrate each year:

'… And upon the Hill of Tynwald sitt in a Chaire covered with a Royall Cloath and Cushions, and your Visage into the East, and your Sword before you holden with the Point upward; your Barrons in the third Degree sitting beside you, and your benificed Men and your Deemsters before you sitting; and your Clarke, your Knights, Esquires and Yeomen, about you in the third Degree; and the worthiest Men in your Land to be called in before your Deemsters, if you will aske any Thing of them, and to hear the Government of your Land, and your Will; and the Commons to stand without the Circle of the Hill, with three Clearkes in their Surplises. And your Deemsters shall make Call in the Coroner of Glanfaba; and he shall call in all the Coroners of Man, and their Yards in their Hands, with their Weapons upon them, either Sword or Axe. And the Moares, that is, to Witt of every Sheading. Then the Chief Coroner, that is the Coroner of Glanfaba, shall make Affence, upon Paine of Life and Lyme, that noe Man make any Disturbance or Stirr in the Time of Tinwald, or any Murmur or Rising in the King's Presence, upon Paine of Hanging and Drawing…'

Even the timing was the same as today. Tynwald was originally held on midsummer's day, then considered to be 24 June, which was also the feast day of St John the Baptist. In Europe there were two main calendars in use, both based on the solar year, i.e. how long it takes the earth to travel once round the sun. Britain used the Julian calendar, named after Julius Ceasar and introduced in 45 BC. Europe used the Gregorian Calendar, named after Pope Gregory VIII who introduced it in 1582. The Gregorian Calendar was more accurate. By the middle of the eighteenth century Britain was nearly a fortnight adrift from the rest of Europe. At that time trade with Europe was increasing significantly and the calendar difference caused endless confusion. Enough was enough and Britain changed to the Gregorian Calendar in 1752 when 3 September was followed by 14 September. This is why today we celebrate Tynwald Day on 5 July and not 24 June. It is also why the church at St John's, linked to Tynwald Hill by the processional way, is dedicated to St John the Baptist.

Separation of ceremony from decision making

Anyone talking about Tynwald today could mean either the ceremony held annually on Tynwald Hill (see pages 22-8), or the Manx parliament which meets regularly to debate and decide laws and policy. It's not possible to determine exactly when legislature and ceremony parted company, but it had certainly happened by 1422. The senior Manxmen of local Things had become the group of senior Manxmen at the national Thing and the number of them had settled into twenty four. The 1422 statute book refers several times to 'the xxiiij' (xxiiij is an old-fashioned way of referring to xxiv or 24), for example: 'Sir John Stanley…asked his Deemsters and the xxiiij the Laws of Man in these points under written…'

Tynwald Hill, St John's showing the processional way to St John's church

These twenty four local leaders became what is now the House of Keys. The Keys still number twenty four and the House of Keys is still referred to in Manx simply as *Yn Kiare as Feed* or 'the four and twenty'. There have been many suggestions as to the origin of the term 'Keys', varying from being a derivation of Norse for 'chosen', or Scottish Gaelic for 'tax', or Irish Gaelic for 'rent', to being the 'key personnel' on the island. In the 1417 statute book the twenty four are referred to in Latin as *claves Manniae et claves legis* – 'the keys of Mann and the keys of the law'. And, at the end of the nineteenth century, historian and Speaker of the House of Keys A.W. Moore believed that the term probably came from the Manx for 'Twenty Four', *kiare-as-feed*, clumsily pronounced by a non-Manx administrator, and then transcribed phonetically as 'keys' by a fifteenth century English clerk who translated it into Latin.

Two sides to Tynwald

For a thousand years or more the Manx, much to their disgust, did not rule the Isle of Man. Those who did rule the island, therefore, had a somewhat ambivalent attitude towards Tynwald. The Keys, as senior local representatives, were almost certainly Manx and so were advocates for anything which benefitted the island, its people and themselves. A foreign ruler therefore – by the fifteenth century that ruler was Englishman Sir John Stanley – may well have been wary of trusting them too far. Very few rulers actually lived on the island so rulers and their

Interior of St John's church showing the seats for the twenty four Keys behind the tables either side of the aisle

representatives gathered about them a group of people, not connected with the Keys, whose advice they felt they might be able to trust. Membership varied but usually included the Bishop of Sodor and Man, the First and Second Deemsters (judges), possibly other senior clerics such as abbots when the island had religious foundations, legal experts such as the Attorney General and senior revenue collectors such as the Receiver General. This group formed the basis of what is now Tynwald's second house, the Legislative Council (LegCo).

Where to meet

The trusted council met wherever the ruler/governor specified, most likely in Castle Rushen. The Keys also met in Castle Rushen occasionally, but more often in one of the members' houses. Not only did the rulers not trust the Keys, the Keys didn't trust the rulers and meeting in a private house provided some protection against unwelcome listeners. Speaking in Manx, a language the rulers never bothered to learn, was also efficacious, although not all senior Manxmen were fluent in the island's language.

In 1706 Bishop Wilson, who was very keen to improve education on the Isle of Man, got permission to build a library near the castle gate in Castletown on the site of what is now the Old House of Keys. It's perhaps worth noting that public libraries were rare in Britain and unknown on Mann, and Bishop Wilson's wish to provide the means of education for everyone (or at least all men) was very unusual. To start with, public libraries consisted mainly of reading rooms, where people could look at the books on offer and read them on site but not take them away. The bishop's new building probably had its book collection on the first floor, with possibly its reading rooms below. From 1710 the Keys met in the lower storey of Bishop Wilson's library, possibly in those reading rooms.

That was all well and good, but no-one seemed to be in charge of maintaining the library building, so by the end of the eighteenth century it was virtually falling down. A Royal Commission of 1792 declared it to be a 'mean, decayed building'. The lower house of Tynwald needed somewhere better to meet.

The Old House of Keys from Castle Rushen

Money troubles

By the middle of the eighteenth century, while the Keys didn't have much acknowledged power, as the most important men in their various local areas they certainly had a lot of influence. Revestment changed all that. For over three hundred years up to 1765 the Isle of Man had been 'ruled' by the Stanley/Athol family with lip service to the British monarch. In 1765 the government at Westminster took over directly in a move now called revestment. Before revestment the Keys had at least some power to legislate and approve money for maintaining harbours etc. After revestment the Westminster parliament wanted all the money it could get its hands on, taxed the island itself, and the Keys lost their authority to raise money by taxation. Put bluntly, Tynwald was skint.

They got round the problem by creating a number of committees which they called boards, each dealing with a different topic and with the authority to raise funding through the rates. It wasn't ideal, but it did help. However it left the Keys with no spare revenue to build themselves a permanent home. After struggling on for another

> **DID YOU KNOW?**
>
> For nearly 150 years from 1750 to 1898, Speakers of the House of Keys were members by blood or marriage of either the Moore or Taubman families.

twenty-five years in Bishop Wilson's library, the Keys resolved that the building was not only unfit, but unsafe and that they should thenceforth hold their meetings in the George Inn. It was like the US Senate or the Russian Duma meeting down the local pub. Discussions for a dedicated meeting place for the Keys were already in train with architect Thomas Brine, but there were arguments about who should pay for it. The Westminster parliament didn't see why it should pay for a meeting chamber for a body it would prefer to be without, while the Keys contended that the cost should be paid out of the revenues paid to Westminster by the

150TH ANNIVERSARY OF THE FIRST GENERAL

150TH ANNIVERSARY OF THE FIRST GENERAL ELECTION OF THE HOUSE OF KEYS

For many years the editors of two local papers, Robert Fargher of Mona's Herald *(above) and James Brown of the* Isle of Man Times *(right) campaigned for a democratic House of Keys*

Isle of Man. Eventually the two sides agreed each to pay part of the costs, the old library building was demolished and the House of Keys, today called the Old House of Keys, built in its place. It was completed in 1821, twenty-nine years after it was first thought necessary.

An elite club

Even hundreds of years after its introduction, Tynwald retained much of the character of the Nordic Things on which it was based. The rites of the ceremony could be traced back to the earliest Tynwalds. The timing of Tynwald day and its accompanying fair agreed with the old calendar. The Keys were drawn from the Isle of Man's premier families, exactly mirroring the senior men representing their local Things. However, somewhere along the way Tynwald had lost the common touch. Since at least the beginning of the seventeenth century the Keys had been an unelected body, or at least unelected by anyone other than themselves. Unless they resigned or, in extreme cases were removed by the other Keys, members of the House of Keys held the post for life. When vacancies occurred, usually by a Key dying, the names of two suitable candidates were presented to the island's governor for him to select one. And of course the governor's hand could be 'forced' by suggesting a totally unacceptable candidate as the second name alongside the Keys' favoured nominee.

> **DID YOU KNOW?**
>
> When campaigning to make the House of Keys an elected body, James Brown called its members Don-keys

To qualify to be one of the Twenty Four a candidate had to be male, over twenty one and hold landed property on the Isle of Man to a certain value per annum. He didn't even need to live on the island. John Curwen, although a scion of one of the leading Manx families, lived at Workington Hall in Cumbria, England. He became a Member of the House of Keys (MHK) in 1781 and the Member of Parliament for Carlisle in Westminster five years later. He was therefore a member of two parliaments at the same time.

While Manx men and women deeply disliked being governed from another country they could see that, across the water, ordinary people were getting a bigger say in what sort of government they had. The 1832 Reform Act passed by the parliament in Westminster greatly increased the number of people in the UK who could vote, and therefore made anyone who wanted to be a member of the UK parliament more directly answerable to those who elected them. Not only had the Manx people no representative at Westminster, but they also had no say in who became a member of the House of Keys.

The editors of two local papers, Robert Fargher of *Mona's Herald* and James Brown of the *Isle of Man Times* (see pictures on previous page) got behind the growing campaign for a House of Keys chosen by the people. At different times both editors went to prison for their views and Brown at least continued to campaign from his cell in Castle Rushen. It was no brief effort. The move to change the House of Keys into a democratically elected chamber went on for more than thirty years.

Turning the Keys to democracy

The turning point was a new Lieutenant Governor. Henry Brougham Loch took up his post as Lieutenant Governor in 1863 and very quickly realised that the Isle of Man needed a way to finance repairs to its own infrastructure without waiting for the Westminster parliament to lumber into action: Tynwald had been unable to raise funds since revestment a century earlier. Harbours, public buildings and roads were in a very poor state as there was no money to pay for repairs. Westminster was uneasy about letting financial control out of its hands – what government isn't? – and found a get-out clause by stating that it was unwilling to hand the control of raising taxes paid by the people to a body not chosen by the people. If the Keys wanted to control

Photograph of Govorner Loch displayed in the chamber of the Legislative Council

the budget, they themselves needed to be controlled through the ballot box.

Governor Loch started a series of delicate negotiations, on the one side with the Twenty Four urging them to vote themselves out of a job, and on the other with Westminster urging it to renounce control of the Manx money. He must have been extremely persuasive as, in 1866, he succeeded and the Isle of Man, Customs, Harbours and Public Purposes Act was passed by Westminster. The Act raised Manx customs duties to match those in the UK, stated that the island would pay £10,000 per year to the British government for providing naval and military protection but confirmed that the island would keep everything it raised

Above: Old Douglas courthouse, the House of Keys' first home in Douglas
Left: the meeting place of Tynwald known to everyone as 'The Wedding Cake'

beyond that sum to spend on infrastructure and repairs. There was a catch of course; the expenditure would be supervised by Westminster and could be vetoed by the Lieutenant Governor, but it was a lot more financial freedom than the Keys had had previously. In return, the House of Keys Election Act was passed on 20 December 1866 by Tynwald. It ended the oligarchic nature of the Keys and provided for public elections.

The Election Act divided the island into ten electoral districts. The six sheadings, Glenfaba, Michael, Ayre, Garff, Middle and Rushen, were to elect three members each, as was the town of Douglas. The towns of Peel, Ramsey and Castletown each elected one member. Men who owned real estate valued at not less than eight pounds, or male tenants paying an annual rent of not less than twelve pounds, were allowed to vote. The first elections for a representative House of Keys took place on 19 March 1867, those elected to serve for a term of seven years. Not all seats were contested and some

MHKs were elected without opposition, but only thirteen of the previous Twenty Four continued to serve in the first elected House of Keys. Some preferred to stand down rather than risk being ousted by popular vote.

Only twelve years later the Keys moved house. They had still been meeting in the House of Keys in Castletown, but the focus of the island was now in the commercial and financial capital, Douglas, and the politicians wanted to be part of it. The Keys moved to Douglas in 1874 but it was not until five years later that they had a settled home. At first they met in the Douglas Courthouse in Athol Street, but found it lacked enough space. Then the Bank of Mona closed leaving its striking building on Prospect Hill vacant. In 1879 the Keys purchased the building and it has been their home ever since.

Changes upstairs

The Keys might have been democratically elected but that didn't mean that the Lieutenant Governor need take any notice of them. The Westminster government still made or ratified all policy decisions, local taxation and expenditure were controlled by the UK Treasury, and officials were appointed by Westminster. Not only that, the members of the Legislative Council (LegCo), which formed the upper chamber of Tynwald, were largely appointed by Westminster too. What is perhaps even more surprising, bearing in mind that this was only a century ago, was that the Lieutenant Governor held much of the real power. He decided everything not already decided by Westminster and, as the man on the spot, had real influence over Westminster decisions too. He could make any such decisions on his own authority without taking the advice of LegCo, and without heeding the wishes of the Keys. What's more, the post of Lieutenant Governor was a job for life if he wanted it.

That changed in 1919 when Sir William Fry was appointed as Lieutenant Governor for a term of seven years. Fry was much more liberal than his predecessor

> **DID YOU KNOW?**
>
> The Speaker's robes are of black silk with golden embroidery (see title page) and were a gift from the Westminster House of Commons in 1966 to commemorate the 100th anniversary of the House of Keys becoming a democratically elected body.

This old staircase is one of the few features dating from when the government building housed the Bank of Mona. It's reputedly haunted

Lord Raglan. One of the first things he allowed was the passing of the House of Keys (Adult Suffrage) Election Act, a resolution that the Keys had been advocating since 1912. It gave the vote to all adults over the age of twenty one; in the UK women under thirty had to wait until 1928 before being allowed to vote. One of universal suffrage's most prominent supporters, William Crennell, MHK for Ramsey, was reported in the *Isle of Man Times* as saying: 'we have been ahead of England in the matter of suffrage for at least thirty years. Long may we remain ahead of her until she comes up to our level'.

The Legislative Council was still a body largely appointed by Westminster, however, so the Constitution Amendment Act was also passed in 1919 bringing some semblance of representation to the upper chamber. In future the Legislative Council was to be made up of the President of Tynwald (until 1990 that was the Lieutenant Governor), the Bishop, the Attorney General and eight other members elected by the House of Keys either from within their number or from elsewhere.

The last steps to (near) independence

Most of the twentieth century saw a gradual transference of power from the Westminster parliament to Tynwald and from unelected officers, such as the Lieutenant Governor, to elected representatives, i.e. the House of Keys. In 1946, for example, an Executive Council was established – its name was changed to the Council of Ministers in 1990 – with members drawn mainly from the Chairmen of the Boards of Tynwald and MHKs.

Legislative building. The large room below the roof is where the Court of Tynwald meets

In 1958 the Westminster Treasury ceased direct control of Manx finances allowing Tynwald, for the first time, to set the Isle of Man's financial policy. In 1987 the island changed from the two hundred year old Board system – arranged so that Tynwald could circumvent the Westminster hold on the purse strings (see page 10) – to a system of government departments each headed by a minister rather than a Chairman.

Today Tynwald is an elected body entirely responsible for governing the internal affairs of Isle of Man. Local people decide by majority which of their neighbours will represent them in making decisions about local laws. It's not that far from the Viking Things of a thousand years ago.

> **DID YOU KNOW?**
>
> In 2006 the voting age for Manx residents was lowered to 16

CHAPTER 2

TYNWALD TODAY

Today the Isle of Man government, loosely referred to as Tynwald, is a trinity of three separate but closely linked elements. The lower house is the House of Keys; the upper house is the Legislative Council; and the two houses sitting together make up the Court of Tynwald.

The House of Keys

There are and have always been twenty-four members of the House of Keys, referred to in Manx simply as *Yn Kiare as Feed* or 'The Four and Twenty'. Since 2016, there have been twelve constituencies in the Isle of Man, each assigned two members elected by popular vote every five years. The constituencies are: Arbory, Castletown and Malew; Ayre and Michael; Douglas Central; Douglas East; Douglas North; Douglas South; Garff; Glenfaba and Peel; Middle; Onchan; Ramsey; Rushen. Roughly seven thousand people in each constituency have the right to vote and, when elections are held, each voter has a maximum of two votes, one for each vacancy in the constituency.

Members of the House of Keys indicate their status by 'MHK' after their name and seating in the chamber is according to constituency. Unlike many parliaments there is no organised 'opposition' and almost all MHKs sit as Independents. Some members may declare an allegiance to a particular political party, but party politics and an enforced vote according to party diktats, such as is the case with the Westminster whip system, has no place in the House of Keys. Members vote according to their own opinions, their constituents' requirements and their conscience.

There are various officers attached to the House of Keys, including messengers, a secretary and a chaplain, but the most famous and most senior is the Speaker. The Speaker of the House of Keys is elected by the MHKs from among the Twenty Four at the first sitting of the Keys after a general election. The Speaker indicates his or her status by 'SHK' after their name.

> **DID YOU KNOW?**
>
> Sir Charles Kerruish served as Speaker of the House of Keys 1962-90. He is the longest serving Speaker of any parliament in the Commonwealth.

The House of Keys chamber. chairs are arranged in alphabetical order of constituency

Despite the name, the Speaker speaks relatively little when the House of Keys is in session; the title is an old form of 'Spokesman' as the Speaker is expected to represent the house as a whole. The Speaker chairs the meetings of the Keys and may vote, although convention dictates that he must vote in favour of continuing the debate or maintaining the status quo, rather than changing it. Reflecting the impartiality of the office, the Speaker is the only member of the House of Keys allowed to abstain from voting.

The Keys meet every Tuesday from the fourth Tuesday in October to the last Tuesday in June. Additional sittings may be called if circumstances or the pressure of business warrant. Members are expected to attend and may only be absent by permission of the Speaker. Most of the time the Keys meet alone, but on the third Tuesday in the month the Keys and the Legislative Council sit together as the Court of Tynwald (see page 19). Unlike in many parliaments, membership of the House of Keys is not a full-time job. The Isle of Man is too small to need twenty-four representatives

Above: the Speakers chair: the date carved at the top is 1890
Right: the snuff box on the Speaker's desk. It dates from 1863 and is decorated with the horns of what is alleged to be a Loaghtan ram. It is still kept filled for use by MHKs

working full time, but, with committees, ministerial work, public visits and all the other things politicians are expected to do, the Keys, like the clergy, really do work more than one day per week.

The main work of the House of Keys

is to make or amend laws. The process of passing new laws can be very slow and involves serious investigation, consultation and debate both in committees of representative Keys ('select committees') and in the House of Keys itself.

Debates in the House are formal and formally controlled. Members stand to indicate to the Speaker that they wish to speak and then stand again when given permission to do so. Manx may be used in the proceedings to indicate fellow MHKs, but is not the language of debate as many MHKs are not fluent Manx speakers. If Manx is used then a translation into English must be provided. If debating a new Bill, the MHK who introduced it may speak at the beginning and the end of the debate. Otherwise no MHK may speak more than once.

Votes are taken by MHKs saying 'aye' or 'no' and, since 2006, by pressing a button indicating 'aye' or 'no' electronically. The results are then officially recorded. All MHKs present, except the Speaker, must vote.

Since March 2018, the House of Keys is also responsible for electing the Chief Minister (who heads the Council of Ministers, similar to the UK Prime Minister and his

The Legislative Council chamber. The public gallery with seating for distinguished visitors, the press and anyone else interested, is in the foreground

Cabinet) from among their number and must do so ten to fourteen days after a general election. Before 2018 the Chief Minister was elected by the Court of Tynwald (see below). The Lieutenant Governor then ratifies the Keys' decision. The Chief Minister specifies who, up to a maximum of nine, are to be Ministers to the various government departments; Ministers can be chosen from members of either house. The nominations are then appointed as Ministers by the Lieutenant Governor. The Council of Ministers collectively decides government policy and advises the Lieutenant Governor.

The Legislative Council

There are eleven members in the Legislative Council: the President of Tynwald, elected by the Keys and the Legislative Council from among their members; the Attorney General and the Bishop of Sodor and Man, who are ex officio members; and eight members elected by the Keys usually from among their number or

> **DID YOU KNOW?**
>
> The only other country which has a Legislative Council is Hong Kong.

occasionally from elsewhere. Members serve for five years, or more if re-elected. Elections are held in February every two or three years, as members are elected in two groups of four to ensure continuity of understanding among the membership.

Members of the Legislative Council indicate their status by 'MLC' after their name and are seated in the chamber according to seniority of service. The President sits in the middle flanked by the Lord Bishop on their right and the Attorney General on their left. The other eight members sit, four on either side, with the longest serving members sitting closest to the middle and the newly elected at the further ends.

As with the Keys, LegCo members are expected to attend meetings of the Legislative Council, and may only be absent by permission of the President. LegCo's main work is to review the Bills introduced by the Keys, make suggestions as to revisions, and correct oversights and flaws if any. Bills may be introduced through LegCo, but nowadays this is only likely to happen when the Keys are in recess.

LegCo sits every Tuesday throughout the year, except on those Tuesdays when it sits with the Keys as the Court of Tynwald (see below). It continues to meet even when the House of Keys is in recess or has been dissolved in anticipation of a general election. However any Bill considered by LegCo after the Keys has been dissolved would have to be reconsidered by the newly elected House of Keys before becoming law.

Debates in the Legislative Council are slightly less formal than in the House of Keys, probably because of the smaller numbers and the personnel involved. It does not mean they are less rigorous. The President controls the proceedings but does not speak in debate; Members do not have to stand to speak, and may speak more than once. Voting takes place much as it does in the House of Keys. Abstentions are not permitted but neither the President nor the Attorney General votes. The former has a casting vote when necessary, the latter may not vote at all.

> **DID YOU KNOW?**
>
> If you hear of someone being in 'another place' it's not some veiled reference to heaven, hell or wishful thinking, but merely the correct form for the Keys to refer to the Legislative Council and vice versa.

This means that, of the nine members who would expect to vote, the Bishop may be in the accidental position of deciding which way that vote goes. However the Bishop of Sodor and Man is appointed in the UK. This makes for the slightly odd circumstances that a UK-appointed post may have the deciding vote in one of the houses in the parliament of a different country. In fact the occasions when this happens are extremely few and, in the past, have only been on minor points.

The Court of Tynwald

The House of Keys and the Legislative Council sit together to form the Court of Tynwald. Members of LegCo sit in a semicircle of chairs near the President on a dias at one end of the Chamber, while the Keys sit in bench seating in the well of the court according to their constituency. The Sword of State is always present on the table when the court is sitting. During the Covid 19 pandemic of 2020-1, when social distancing was being advocated, half the Keys sat in alternate chairs in the main body of the hall, while the rest used the public gallery, which was of course away from their electronic voting stations. Voting necessitated a two-stage process whereby those seated in the well voted first, then evacuated the chamber, allowing those seated in the public gallery to descend and themselves vote. Social distancing was maintained at all times, but the process was long winded in the extreme.

On the far left of the Legislative Council (see picture opposite) hangs Charles Kerruish's coat of arms, beneath his portrait. The keys and the sword of state explain themselves, while at the top, Odin's raven is holding a snowdrop, Charles' mother's favourite flower. The motto is in Manx and is a reference to the Manx motto quocunque jeceris stabit *('whichever way you throw me I stand'). Loosely translated Kerruish's motto* ny cur y cass orrym *means 'don't tread on me'*

The Court of Tynwald, taken from the public gallery

The Court meets every third Tuesday in the month from October to June, plus the Tuesday after Tynwald Day (5 July). Tynwald Court is principally concerned with answering questions, deliberating finance, receiving and debating reports of committees or government departments, discussing formal proposals and signing Bills, which both the President of Tynwald and the Speaker of the House of Keys must sign. Sittings can be as long as three consecutive days depending on the volume of business, and further sittings can be summoned by the President or requested by a quorum of either House.

Debates follow very much the procedure used in the House of Keys (see above) except that proceedings are controlled by the President of Tynwald and not the Speaker of the House of Keys. In the Court of Tynwald the Speaker has the same voting rights as any other MHK.

Voting takes place orally and electronically as described above, but voting procedures are more complex. According to the most recently published Tynwald Companion (2016): 'a motion is carried if a majority of both the House of Keys and the Legislative Council, counted separately, are in favour. Where there is an equality of votes in the Legislative Council, the President has a casting vote, but will only vote to ensure the Legislative Council vote is the same as that of the House of Keys. If both Branches are tied, because there is an equality of votes in the House of Keys the motion is considered lost and so the President's casting vote is used against the motion, which fails. When a majority in each of the Branches have [sic] voted differently, in favour or not, a motion is thereby lost. However, if lost in Council, the mover of the motion can use a procedure for a joint vote of all Members at a following sitting.' The process is designed to ensure that the Legislative Council, whose members are either elected by the Keys or appointed by the British crown, may delay but cannot overturn something passed by the House of Keys, whose members are elected by popular vote in the Isle of Man.

When the work planned for any session of the Court of Tynwald is completed, the President and the Legislative Council leave. If the House of Keys has any further business to consider it may continue sitting, although this is unusual.

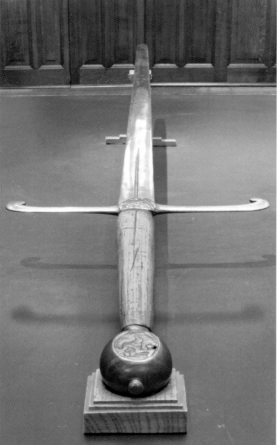

All three

Accurate records, known as Hansard (after Thomas Hansard who was the first official printer to the Westminster parliament) of the meetings in all three debating chambers are made by using speech recognition technology. Voice profiles of everyone entitled to speak in the Court of Tynwald

> **DID YOU KNOW?**
>
> The Tynwald Hansard team also produces transcripts for the parliaments of Guernsey, Gibralter, Alderney, Sark, and the Turks & Caicos Islands.

are recorded at the beginning of the parliamentary year, so that the programme can recognise and understand each members' patterns of speech and convert them automatically into text. The Tynwald Hansard editorial team then checks the transcript carefully against the original recording to produce an essentially verbatim report. Grammar may be corrected and repetition removed but that is all.

Anyone interested may watch debates from the public gallery in any of the three chambers. Alternatively those interested can listen to live debates streamed online.

Above: the Manx Sword of State (Photograph © Tynwald)
Right: the Governor's Box in the Distinguished Strangers' Gallery. The Lieutenant Governor may attend a sitting of the Court of Tynwald whenever he or she wishes but may take no part in the proceedings

CHAPTER 3

THE PEOPLE ON THE HILL

You may go to the ends of Europe and see nothing of the kind that is half so interesting…' Thus wrote Hall Caine, famous Victorian novelist and MHK for Ramsey. The open-air meeting of Tynwald takes place as it has done for hundreds of years at Tynwald Hill in St John's each 5 July or, if that is a Sunday, on 6 July. For such a famous occasion, rather a lot of what happens, doesn't happen on the Hill.

> **DID YOU KNOW?**
>
> In keeping with the Viking idea of hospitality and truce, Tynwald Hill is said to contain earth drawn from all seventeen parishes in the island. Not only the people but also the land on which they live are therefore all represented on the ancient hill in St John's.

Starting the day

The official proceedings begin when the Lord of Man or their representative arrives at Tynwald Green, the greensward between the Royal Chapel of St John the Baptist and Tynwald Hill. The Lord of Man is the British monarch. He or she is occasionally represented by a member of their family, but usually their official representative, the island's Lieutenant Governor, attends on their behalf.

Whoever is officiating is usually greeted by some form of pomp and circumstance, but the real business of the day starts when they lay a wreath at the National War Memorial on the north side of the processional way. The Last Post is played and officials, guests and spectators stand for a minute's silence which ends with the wake-up call Reveille.

The Lieutenant Governor and dignitaries then process to the hall next to the Royal Chapel which is used as the Robing Room. From there they make their way into the Royal Chapel for a short ecumenical service conducted primarily in English, although parts of it are in Manx. Representatives of all Christian denominations take part and the proceedings are relayed by speaker to spectators outside who are invited to join in the hymns and responses.

The procession

On the conclusion of the service, dignitaries proceed in twos from the Royal Chapel along the processional way mostly in reverse order of seniority. The Lord of Man or their representative is preceded by the Manx Sword of State carried, point upwards, by the swordbearer (see opposite and page 7). Just before the war memorial the procession halts and faces inwards so that the Lieutenant Governor can pass between them. The procession effectively turns itself inside out so that the Lieutenant Governor, one of the last to leave the Royal Chapel, is nevertheless the first to step onto Tynwald Hill.

Sir Richard Gozney, the island's Lieutenant Governor 2016-21, cuts a lonely figure as he lays a wreath at the war memorial during the Tynwald ceremony of 2020. The coronavirus pandemic was raging and the usual crowds were missing but nothing was forgotten

The processional way is strewn with marram grass, the local name for which is 'bent', or in Manx *shastagh-traie*. According to Manx tradition, Manannan, the Celtic god of the sea and the Isle of Man's traditional protector, was thought to expect bent as an annual tribute on midsummer's eve. 5 July is old midsummer's day (see page 8), so propitiating a touchy seagod, particularly one with such an affinity to the weather, might seem to be a good safeguard against unwanted disturbances to Tynwald Day.

Another Manx tradition is that everyone attending Tynwald, not only dignitaries but also spectators, should wear a buttonhole of *bollan bane* or mugwort. Traditionally worn in the hat or on the head, mugwort protects against supernatural harm. By Scandinavian custom, wearers of bollan bane are also demonstrating loyalty to their monarch.

Who sits where and who does what

Tynwald Hill is formed of four tiers, each slightly smaller than the one below it. Seating on the Hill is determined by historic precedent, with those viewed as more important sitting higher up, although such divisions have less weight today. Only the top level is covered by a canvas canopy – in 2020, pandemic year, there was no canopy at all – so on rainy Tynwald Days many dignitaries and their finery get wet. Being held in July the weather is usually kind, but there are, of course, always exceptions.

On top of the Hill sits the Lord of Man or their representative and/or the Lieutenant Governor. Sitting with the Lieutenant Governor are the President of Tynwald,

Above: from 1998 to 2021, the official swordbearer at Tynwald was Bernadette Williams. She is the first woman to have held the post Left: empty seating on the Hill as dignitaries process towards it. Note the Royal Standard, with the three-point label, the first and third points charged with the Cross of St George, the second point charged with the red heart. Usually the three Legs of Man is flown above Tynwald Hill, but, in 2021, Princess Anne the Princess Royal, whose Standard this is, represented Her Majesty the Queen at Tynwald.

the Bishop of Sodor and Man, members of the Legislative Council, the Clerk of the Legislative Council, the Seneschal, the Swordbearer, the Surgeon to the Household and the Lieutenant Governor's private secretary. The word 'seneschal' comes from mediaeval French and, at its most general, means 'overseer'. In Tynwald the Seneschal is responsible for the messengers, security guards and the fabric of the buildings. The Surgeon to the Household – the household in question is the royal household – is an ancient appointment which now means the medic who looks after the Lieutenant Governor and family, plus visiting dignitaries if they need medical attention. The Surgeon of the Household usually combines this role with their 'day job' at Noble's Hospital.

The Speaker and Members of the House of Keys and their Chaplain sit on the second tier of Tynwald Hill, together with the Clerk of Tynwald who is also Secretary of the House of Keys.

The third tier is occupied by the High Bailiff, a representative of the Commission of the Peace, the Chief Registrar, the Mayor of Douglas, the chairmen or women of the town and village commissioners, the Archdeacon, the Vicar General, the Roman Catholic Dean, representatives of the free churches and the Salvation Army, the Chief Secretary and the Chief Constable. The High Bailiff is the head stipendiary magistrate and therefore a judicial officer in the High Court of Justice. The Archdeacon of Man is second only to the

Bob Carswell, Yn Lhaihder, fencing the court

bishop within the diocese, while the Vicar General is a judge in the ecclesiastical courts and represents the church in legal matters. The Chief Secretary is the head of the Isle of Man's civil service.

The coroners sit on the fourth and lowest tier of the Hill, with Yn Lhaihder (The Reader), the captains of the parishes, the Deemsters, the Judge of Appeal and the Superintendent of Police. Also on the fourth tier are the two lecterns used during the proceedings. The coroners on the Isle of Man are not like coroners in the UK who are coroners of inquests inquiring into unnatural deaths; that role is taken by the High Bailiff or their deputy. Manx coroners are responsible for ensuring that the work of the court is carried out, which includes summonsing jurors and enforcing court judgments, including collecting fines. Deemsters are the Isle of Man judges. There are seventeen parishes on Mann and therefore seventeen captains of the parish, a title which is held until death. Historically the captains were responsible for civil defence and organising militia, but today the post is largely ceremonial although captains are expected to take a lead in parish events.

Yn Lhaihder is possibly unique among all government officials, as the post is the only one whose official title has always been in Manx. The history of Yn Lhaihder is obscure but one or two things seem likely. Up until the first half of the seventeenth century Manx was purely an oral language – it was not written down. A reader has to have something to read and, in view of the Manx title, Yn Lhaihder presumably has to have something to read in Manx. The post cannot therefore be more than four hundred years old and many experts think it much more recent, possibly only within the last century. Two other organisations have the post of Reader: academia and the church. Readers were important in areas or for languages where literacy was rare and information needed to be imparted.

On Tynwald Hill

When everyone is in position the Lieutenant Governor invites the First Deemster to direct that the court be fenced. Fencing the court goes all the way back to the Viking Things (see page 5). It is the equivalent of declaring a truce within a certain area and for the duration of the court meeting. 'Fencing' has nothing to do with erecting a physical barrier, but comes from a fourteenth century French word *defens* from which we get the English 'defend' and 'defence'. The intention of fencing the court is to protect it and, traditionally, no weapons apart from the Sword of State – which is itself blunted – were permitted within the symbolic fence.

> **DID YOU KNOW?**
>
> In recent years, two British monarchs have attended on Tynwald Hill in person. HM Queen Elizabeth presided in Manx millennium year 1979 and also in 2003; her father King George VI presided in 1945.

The First Deemster directs that the Chief Coroner, which is that of Glenfaba and Michael, and Yn Lhaihder fence the court. The Coroner then fences the court to '…charge that no person do quarrel, brawl or make any disturbance and that all persons do answer their names when called…' He speaks in English to 'charge this whole audience to bear witness this Court is now fenced'. As soon as he's finished speaking, Yn Lhaihder fences the court in Manx, concluding with the same injunction: *Ta mee cur recortys er y clane eanish shoh dy vel yn Whaiyl shoh nishtagh fo harey.*

Once the court is fenced the coroners leave their seats on the fourth tier and climb the steps of the Hill where they kneel to be sworn in and receive their staves of office. The four coroners represent the six sheadings: Glenfaba and Michael, Ayre and Garff, Middle, Rushen. The word sheading is most often thought to come from the Norse *skeið*, an ocean-going warship with thirty benches, which needed sixty rowers and therefore had a crew of about eighty. Under the Norse law of *leiðangr*, a leader could expect groups of people living in areas of a certain size to provide warships and enough men to crew them. The name for the ship therefore became the name for land of a certain area. Whatever the derivation of the word, the sheadings have formed the basis of the island's organisation and administration ever since the time of the Vikings. Even today, the modern constituency map is based on the ancient sheadings.

The coroners ascending the hill to be sworn in

Once the coroners have been sworn in, the Lieutenant Governor asks the 'learned Deemsters' to proclaim the laws which have been passed in the past year. At one time the laws were proclaimed in their entirety, which was often the first time the listening crowd knew what the new laws were. Today each law's title and brief summary is all that is read. The First Deemster stands at the lectern nearer the main road, and proclaims the news laws in English. The Second Deemster stands at the lectern nearer the war memorial and proclaims the new laws in Manx. If the Second Deemster is not available then Yn Lhaihder takes their place.

New Acts can become law as soon as they have received royal assent, but must be promulgated from Tynwald Hill within eighteen months of enactment or they cease to be laws. It used to be the case that, regardless of when they received royal assent, new Acts could not pass into law until after being read on Tynwald Hill. In 1904 when the Isle of Man agreed at short notice to host international motor trials, legislation was rushed through in March and the trials were scheduled for 10 May. The next planned Tynwald Day was, of course, in July, *after* the date set for the trials. To make everything legal they had to organise an extra Tynwald Day and so, on 5 May 1904, all necessary personnel met on Tynwald Hill to promulgate the Highways (Light Locomotive) Act. Those motor trials eventually became the Manx TT.

DID YOU KNOW?

St John's is in the parish of German, so it could be said that Manx laws are read in English, in Manx and in German!

The laws being promulgated from Tynwald Hill, 2020. Compare this with the usual scene pictured on page 24. The pandemic regulations meant a 'stripped down' Tynwald, but the essentials of the ancient ceremony remained unchanged

Once all the new laws have been promulgated the Lieutenant Governor invites members of the public to approach with Petitions for Redress. Sometimes known as Tynwald Hill petitions, these are grievances presented directly to parliament on matters which individuals think would be to the public good to resolve. Petitions must be in writing, in a particular form – guidance is available from the Clerk of Tynwald and online – and signed with the petitioner(s) name and address(es). Those with Petitions for Redress approach the Hill along the processional way, and the Clerk of Tynwald leaves his seat next to the Speaker of the House of Keys, and goes down the steps of the Hill to meet them. The Clerk collects the petitions and takes them to the Lieutenant Governor before resuming his seat. Petitioning for Redress is an ancient right of the Manx people but had largely fallen into disuse until the 1950s when the practice was revived. Petitions for Redress are considered by the Standing Orders Committee of Tynwald and may eventually lead to changes in the law.

For the first time certainly in living memory and possibly ever, Petitions for Redress were not made in person at the Tynwald ceremony of 2020. The island was still subject to some of the social restrictions imposed as a result of the Covid 19 pandemic, so the Tynwald ceremony was stripped down to the essentials and attendance at the Hill by politicians not directly involved, as well as members of the public was discouraged. Instead Petitions for Redress were submitted to the Clerk of Tynwald's Office by 5pm on Wednesday 1 July. The Clerk of Tynwald then presented the petitions on the petitioners' behalf. Presenting Petitions of Redress in person resumed at the Tynwald ceremony the following year.

The Royal Chapel

The business on Tynwald Hill ends with the presentation and receipt of the Petitions for Redress. The dignitaries and officials then leave the Hill and proceed back to the church at the other end of the processional way, in much the same way as they processed from it, i.e. in reverse order of historic importance. The Church of St John the Baptist stands on the site of what was once a chapel in the parish of German. Until the beginning of the nineteenth century the chapel's main function was that of a courthouse. The current building dates from 1849 but its status was still that of a chapel in the parish of German. It was not until exactly one hundred years later, in 1949, that the ecclesiastical parish of St John's was formed and 'her majesty's royal or free chapel of St John the Baptist' became the parish church. It is also still the place where the Court of Tynwald meets on Tynwald Day.

Once the various dignitaries have made their way from Tynwald Hill to the Royal Chapel, they meet for a sitting of the Court of Tynwald. It's important to remember that, legally, this sitting of the Court of Tynwald is no different from the regular sittings held throughout the year in the Legislative Buildings in Douglas (see page 19). The Lieutenant Governor therefore attends as a guest of the Court but takes no part in the proceedings.

The main reason for this sitting of Tynwald Court is for the laws just read out from Tynwald Hill to be captioned or signed. All laws are signed first by the President of Tynwald and then by the Speaker of the House of Keys. If someone is to be awarded the Tynwald Honour Medal, which is the highest award Tynwald can bestow, then it will be awarded after the captioning of the laws.

The business of the Court of Tynwald is then concluded and the Lieutenant Governor and the Legislative Council withdraw. The House of Keys remains formally to conclude the business before it too leaves the Royal Chapel, probably to enjoy the traditional Tynwald Day fair.

> **DID YOU KNOW?**
>
> The British Monarch is the Lord of Man, even if the monarch is female. Queen Victoria preferred to be addressed as the Lady of Man but it was never her official title.

Tynwald Fair

CHAPTER 4

OTHER THINGS...

Most of the political and legal arrangements of the Isle of Man can be traced directly to the organisation of the Norsemen. A seafaring and warlike community, the Viking journeyings took them to much of northern Europe and even across the Atlantic. They took their social organisation with them, particularly their Things (see page 5). Shetland and Orkney once had their parliaments, both at places called Tingwall. There is even a town of Dingwall at the end of Cromarty Firth in the Highland of Scotland, so it is not surprising that the Isle of Man is not the only country to remember this in the name of its parliament. But, apart from the name, how much of the original arrangement of Viking Things remains?

Norway

Most of the Vikings who invaded Mann and, incidentally, Ireland, South Wales, the Faroe Islands and Iceland, came originally from what is now Norway. At various times in its history Norway has been ruled by or in union with Denmark or Sweden, so its parliamentary history is slightly bumpy.

In the ninth and tenth centuries Things were certainly established as regional assemblies and, by the fourteenth century, the four major assemblies Frostating, Gulating, Eidsivating and Borgarting were amalgamated on the orders of King Magnus Lagabøte ('lawmender') to ensure that the same rules applied throughout Norway.

The building on the right is the Norwegian Storting, Oslo (Photograph © Information and Documentation Department of the Norwegian Storting)

In 1660, Danish King Frederick III became absolute monarch and the ancient laws were superseded. Rule by monarch continued until Norway's written constitution was drawn up in 1814, when Denmark passed Norway to Sweden, and the Norwegian parliament, the Storting, was established. The word revived the idea of the Things from a thousand years previously. *Stor* is Norwegian for 'great', so *Storting* is 'great assembly'.

The Storting is a unicameral or single chamber parliament with a fixed length. It cannot be dissolved early and there are no bye elections. Elections are held every four years and votes are for political parties, not individuals. The 169 seats are then allocated according to the proportion of the vote each party has received. Should a seat become vacant during the term of a parliament, the next candidate on the party election list who would have had a seat had the party gained enough votes, serves to the end of the parliament.

> **DID YOU KNOW?**
>
> The Norwegian constitution is the second oldest written constitution in the world. The oldest is that of the United States of America.

Iceland

Iceland's Alþingi was established about 930 at Þingvellir ('Assembly field') on the Norwegian pattern and so seemed to be very similar to the Tynwald of the time: the country's leaders met to make laws and dispense justice while their communities traded, played games and sports (see page 4), and probably drank too much. *Al* is Norse for general, so *Alþingi* is 'general assembly'.

The Alþingi remained as Iceland's parliament until the vagaries of royal succession in the late fourteenth

Above: Parliament House, home to the Icelandic Alþingi, Reykjavik (Photograph © Secretariat of Althingi Parliament of Iceland)
Left: The Þingvellir, marked by the flag, was the site of Iceland's parliament from 930 to 1798

century brought both Norway and Iceland under the rule of Denmark. After that, for the next five hundred years, the Alþingi served as a court, upholding legislation but not passing it. In 1799 it was disbanded completely.

A new Alþingi was established in 1845, but as a consultative assembly only. Iceland was still under Danish rule and changes to the law could only be made in Copenhagen. In 1874 the new Alþingi was granted limited independence and the power to pass laws on exclusively Icelandic matters. What is interesting from the Tynwald point of view is that the 1874 Alþingi had two chambers, the lower one (*nedri deild* or 'lower division') an elected chamber of twenty-four, the upper one (*efri deild* or 'upper division') with six elected members and six members appointed by the Danish government. The arrangement is very similar to the arrangement of Tynwald and its relationship with the UK government at the time.

The constitution of the Alþingi changed radically over the following century, not least because Iceland became *de facto* independent when Germany invaded Denmark on 9 April 1940. Independence was confirmed and the Republic of Iceland created on 17 June 1944 when the Alþingi met at its ancient assembly field at Þingvellir probably for the first time since 1798. Since then the Alþingi has changed radically. It is now a single legislative chamber with sixty-three members elected every four years based on a party-list proportional representation system similar to that of Norway.

Denmark

Things have probably been part of Danish administration for over a thousand years, but from the eleventh to the seventeenth century were regional assemblies, Landstings, making local laws. *Land* is the equivalent of 'county' or 'specific area', so *Landstings* were a bit like an English county council.

Denmark became a constitutional monarchy on 5 June 1849 with a new parliament called the Rigsdagen ('imperial assembly'). The Rigsdagen had two chambers, the Folketing elected by the general population, and the Landsting, which retained the old name and was elected by landowners. The two had equal power and, over the years the lack of clarity between their different functions led to duplication of effort or simply rubber stamping.

In 1953 a new constitution was agreed by referendum, changing the parliament into a unicameral or single chamber assembly called the Folketing or 'people's assembly'. The Folketing has 179 members and an extremely complicated voting system based on proportional representation but also ensuring that regions are fairly represented.

Greenland

Vikings from Norway settled in Greenland in the tenth century and lived there for over 450 years. Sometime before 1500, the Norse settlements died out, possibly because a change in climate made the weather very much colder. Greenland had not been forgotten in Scandinavia, however, and was recolonized by Denmark early in the eighteenth century, becoming officially Danish in 1814. In 1911 Landstings ('area assemblies') were introduced, one each for North and South Greenland. However legislation continued to be passed in Denmark, where Greenland had no representation, and in 1953 Greenland was fully integrated into the Danish state.

In 1979 Greenland was granted home rule, with the new parliament being called the Landsting. Self government came on

The Danish Folketing, Copenhagan (Photograph © Information Office of the Danish Parliament)

21 June 2009 when the Danish word Landsting was replaced by the Greenlandish (Inuit) word Inatsisartut meaning 'those who make laws', although it's often still referred to as the Landsting by Danish speakers. Greenland is not entirely independent, as judicial, defence and monetary policy is still decided in Denmark, and the Inatsisartut may not pass any law which contravenes the Danish constitution. The Inatsisartut/Landsting is a single chamber of thirty-one members elected by the whole of Greenland – there are no constituencies – by a system of proportional representation. It meets in autumn and spring for two to three months.

Faroe Islands

Like the Isle of Man, the Faroe Islands were invaded by Vikings from Norway who imported their Thing system. As the Faroe Islands are closer to Norway than Iceland it is also possible that the Faroese Alþingi predates the Icelandic one. The Faroe Islands remained largely self governing until the late thirteenth century when the Norwegian *landsløg*, or land law, was introduced. The Faroese Løgting ('law assembly') then had the function of a court rather than a legislative body. Political jockeying brought Norway, and hence the Faroe Islands, under the rule of Denmark, but little changed until the institution of King Frederick III's absolute monarchy in 1660 (see Norway above). The Faroese Løgting ceased to have any real influence and was abolished entirely in 1816, when Danish rule turned the Faroe Islands into the equivalent of an *amt* or 'county'. In 1852 the Løgting was reinstated but could only act in an advisory capacity.

> DID YOU KNOW?
>
> Greenland is the largest island in the world and, at 57,000, is the least densely populated country.

Germany invaded Denmark on 9 April 1940 and, three days later, Britain established a base on the Faroe Islands to protect shipping. The Løgting became the Faroese legislative assembly and the Islands ran themselves for the rest of the war. At the end of hostilities Denmark had little choice but to agree to a much greater amount of autonomy. The Løgting is a unicameral legislative assembly with thirty-three members elected for a four-year term by proportional representation.

Finland

Finland's parliament is the Suomen Eduskunta, but Finland also has a Thing. For much of their history Sweden and Finland were the same country, although ethnically diverse. Then, in 1809, Russia conquered Finland. When Finland gained its independence a century later in 1917, a substantial number of ethnic Swedes still lived in the new country. Consequently, in 1919, the Folkting or Swedish Assembly of Finland was established to promote the language and rights of Finland's Swedish speaking population, in particular in legal matters and court hearings.

The Folkting ('people's assembly') has seventy-five members who serve for a term of four years. Sixty-eight members are elected via municipal elections and seven appointed by the Lagting of the Åland Islands (see below). The distribution of seats is based on the number of votes accrued by ethnic Swedish candidates in municipal elections with individuals then appointed by their party. Voters cannot therefore elect candidates directly to the Folkting.

Åland Islands

The Åland Islands are a Swedish speaking autonomous region of Finland, with its own parliament, the Lagting ('law assembly'), which first sat in 1922. It is unicameral with thirty members elected for four years by proportional representation. It is responsible for legislation and administration for everything except foreign/defence policies and taxation. These rest with the Finnish parliament to which the Åland Islands sends one parliamentary representative.

Interestingly, just as Manx citizens have the right to present Petitions for Redress directly to Parliament on Tynwald Hill (see page 27), Åland Islanders can present a Citizens' Initiative directly to their Lagting. Such an initiative requires 1,000 signatories (out of a population of just under 30,000) on the paperwork. As with Petitions for Redress to Tynwald, such Citizens' Initiatives must be considered in committee and may possibly lead to a change in the law.

The Lagting of the Åland Islands, Mariehamn,
(Photograph © Åland Islands)

THE
RIOT
AND THE
DANCE

ADVENTURE BOOK

WITH DR. GORDON WILSON

ADAPTED FROM THE THEATRICAL DOCUMENTARY BY N.D. WILSON

canonpress
CANONPRESS.COM
MOSCOW IDAHO

LOCATIONS:

Published by Canon Press
P.O. Box 8729, Moscow, ID 83843
800.488.2034 | www.canonpress.com

The Riot and the Dance Adventure Book, adapted from the theatrical
documentary (Gorilla Poet Productions, March 2018) by N.D. Wilson.

Cover and interior design by James Engerbretson.

Library of Congress Cataloging-in-Publication Data is forthcoming.

SETTING OUT

Put on your biggest pair of boots and step outside. Search in the grass for beetle caves and worm holes.

Try to spot the glint of a spider web in a juniper bush, and look for the owner. She will be sitting nervously in her funnel, hoping you go away.

If you live in a city, look up for a hawk. He will be riding the wind and waiting to devour one of those purple-necked pigeons.

Everything you see is made of words. That's how God created it all in the beginning (Gen. 1). That's how it still is today. And the best Word of all—the one Word who actually is God—is Jesus. He is the reason everything is here (Jn. 1).

So, when you step outside, you're on a hunt—a Word hunt. And every little creature-word you find tells you about the one true Creator.

3

We humans are the most important of God's creatures. God put the first man and the first woman in charge of all the other created things—naming, ruling, tending, exploring, watching, subduing, improving the rest of the world. That's been our job ever since (Gen. 1:27-29).

This is Dr. Gordon Wilson. He is a biologist, which is a great career for a kid who grew up catching and investigating every creature he could find. In case you couldn't tell, he is also a human. He has chased other creatures on mountains, in deserts, under oceans, and in forests and jungles. (He has only been bitten a few times.)

You too can go to the tops of the mountains or down to the floors of seas or into the depths of jungles—as soon as you can buy your own jeep and scuba equipment. Until then, come with us on Dr. Wilson's adventures. He took plenty of pictures.

Because Christians believe God made the world, we are supposed to look for God's good design in His creations. But this is not how most biologists act. They think it's their job to explain the world without God. They say that all life came about by means of chance and the death of the losers in the struggle to survive.

Death is a part of the story God is telling—but it's the part of the story ruined by sin. What comes after death is much more important: resurrection.

So the world is broken, but it will be healed. Where evolutionary scientists only see survival of the fittest, Christians should see the riot and dance, as all of creation works in concert to praise its Creator.

PACIFIC NORTHWEST

So, where should we start?

Your eyes are not yet sharp enough for the jungle, and your reflexes are not yet quick enough for the cobra. So, stand and breathe wherever you are. Focus your senses on the mini-masterpieces the Great Artist has painted in your own little corner of the world. And then, follow us out into the riot and the dance.

Welcome to what is right outside Dr. Wilson's door—the pine forests of the Pacific Northwest. This tiny pine-tree farmer was the size of a pink peanut when she was born. She's a red squirrel, and she can jump, strip pine cones for food, and plant forests with the seeds she buries or drops. (She is not the tidiest eater.)

You may know that trees grow through photosynthesis, but what does that mean? Each branchy giant was grown mostly out of thin air with star power from the sun's light. The only other major thing a pine tree needs besides light is water, which has flown above the earth in clouds, and then fallen to the soil as rain, and then been evaporated up into the sky again, only to fall again (maybe on your front yard).

Follow a pine seed as it falls from the starlit tree-tops. It has landed near a miniature riot, where hairy, armored yellow-jackets are feasting on a dead earthworm. People scramble away from yellow-jackets, but the next time one lands on your picnic lunch, sit still long enough to imagine if it were twenty times your size. Imagine being brave enough to bite it on the head or grab its belly, barely out of stinger's reach. That's what these ants are doing.

Don't leave to find exotic beasts until you find a neighborhood pond or stream. Even if you've seen it a hundred times, no local water is "boring"—there is more wildlife there than in any zoo.

This is a Columbia spotted frog. It was hiding in Dr. Wilson's favorite mountain pond. Frogs can hibernate, surviving even Alaskan winters. They can also estivate, which is a long word that means "sleep until the rains come again and it stops being dangerously hot and dry."

Make sure you also net a few water striders. The feet of these "true bugs" are covered in waxy microhairs that allow them to skip on water without sinking. They use their sharp, straw-like beaks to slurp up the juices of any hapless insect that falls into their watery domain.

Garter snakes are probably the most common snakes in North America. This big garter's bite wouldn't hurt any more than your brother snapping you with a rubber band, and little garters almost never even try, so you can certainly catch one. (Just be sure you don't mistake a venomous species for a harmless garter!) If you do grab a garter—firmly right behind his head is best—prepare yourself for the foul-smelling musk that the terrified creature will smear onto your hand. It's his only other defense.

If Dr. Wilson were to go north and east from his home, to Canada, we could find tens of thousands of red-sided garter snakes wintering together like snake spaghetti in the Narcisse Snake Pits. But we'll leave that for you to do on your own.

MOUNTAINS OF MONTANA

Next, we go up and away to the mountain tops. It's still close to home for Dr. Wilson, but he couldn't live here: He'd need to grow a thick fur coat to survive temperatures as cold as sixty degrees below zero. When it's this cold, you can throw a boiling pot of water into the air and it will turn into snow. When it's this cold, any exposed skin can freeze in only ten minutes.

Where God smashes huge tectonic plates together to make the soaring mountains, He also likes to put impressive beasts. This is a bighorn sheep. If you spend most of your time on the cliffs, you're usually safe from predators. So, bighorns don't worry about much besides eating and fighting. Bighorn rams live to headbutt other rams, crashing into each other at automobile speeds over and over again, sometimes continuing all day and all night.

Naming animals has been people's job since the beginning, and it's not hard to see why we called these creatures pronghorn antelope (although they are more like giraffes and okapis than antelope or deer.)

God designed pronghorns to be four-legged landbirds: hollow hairs and light-weight bones make them the fastest creature in this hemisphere. A pronghorn can gallop at 55 miles per hour, winging over the earth long enough to leave coyotes, cougars, and wolves far behind. Their extreme speed came in handy when they were hunted by North American cheetahs (which are now extinct).

A grown moose is taller than Dr. Wilson at its shoulder. It's the tallest creature on this half of the globe. A moose is the Creator's perfectly huge match for the mountains themselves.

Moose also have huge appetites. If you loved salad and had it for lunch and then for dinner, you might eat a pound of it. A moose, however, could eat fifty pounds of lettuce in one day and still have room for more. No wonder people despair when moose get into their gardens.

Moose love winter best, because the cold kills ticks...and a moose can get stuck carrying more than 75,000 of the blood-sucking parasites!

The moose may be tallest, but the American bison is the heaviest animal in these parts. A bison is as heavy as a car—1,400 pounds of western nobility and comedy combined under a big woolly rug.

Bison used to stretch over the continent from Alaska to Mexico by the millions, but by the 1880s there were less than a hundred left in the wild. (This was caused by overhunting, the transformation of the Great Plains, and malignant new cow diseases.)

Thanks to Teddy Roosevelt, the Bronx Zoo, and others, bison did not go extinct. Now, there is a small but stable number of perhaps thirty thousand bison living in the United States.

PACIFIC COAST

Time to head farther west, swapping the mountain snows for the seaside rains. Here, on the Pacific Coast, God has been using the sun to build giant wooden skyscrapers that are older than the modern world: the coast redwoods. The largest of these trees needs more than a billion needles to stay healthy. The oldest coast redwood sprouted two centuries before Jesus.

If God has spent more than two thousand years making something grow, we can give it a second glance. Look at that picture again... The dry mass of one of these trees is more than 400 tons. That's more than the weight of 500 bison, or one million red squirrels—all of it gathered out of thin air by the needles and powered by our sun.

15

Next, turn toward the sea breeze, and skootch off the edge of the continent and down the cliffs to sea level. Few animals have more cuteness than harbor seals. These are the most common variety of seals on the globe, and this pod has chosen a sandy spit on the central Oregon coast.

Harbor seals swim and dive from birth and are short, soft, and playful. This particular herd of seals has few worries besides catching food and being itchy.

Elephant seals are not so carefree. Yes, they jiggle and their noses fall into their mouths. But in an elephant seal herd, five-thousand-pound bulls attack females and drive bachelors away. Half-ton mother elephant seals accidentally crush their young, who are then devoured by seagulls. Orphaned pups get bitten and chewed to death.

As Christians, we know this is not how the world was meant to be. This is the result of the Fall.

Paul wrote that all creation groans for redemption, crying out to be made new. He saw it then, and we can see it now. The world is often more riot than dance. But we can take some comfort from this:

This is not how the beaches will be run in the resurrection.

SONORAN DESERT & SANTA RITA MOUNTAINS

How much of our broken world does God love? All of it. Every prickle and every pebble. Every storm and every breeze. Every claw and every scale. Even when you look small, God's glory is big.

We have filled our canteens and left the ocean behind us. This is the Sonoran Desert, where coyotes stretch and yawn among the saguaros. It is over 100,000 square miles, twice the size of New York State, and it's a one-of-a-kind place for finding new creatures. Walk lightly, though—many of them have fangs.

You're not likely to catch a zebra-tailed lizard with your hands. They are probably the fastest lizards in North America, and perhaps the most handsome. This male has turquoise and salmon colors, a shovel-nose for burrowing in the sand, and, of course, zebra striping on his tail. He waves his stripes like a banner when he's not in a hurry.

The best way to catch a lizard without hurting either of you is by tying a copper-wire noose to a long stick. This little guy was so focused on making sure Dr. Wilson didn't get too close that he let the bright loop settle over his shoulders.

Sometimes, once you've caught a lizard, you can soothe him to sleep with a nice belly rub.

20

The Sonoran Desert is full of snakes. (And don't you go trying to catch them with wire nooses. Get Dr. Wilson to show you how to use snake tongs sometime.) The fastest and the grouchiest is the coachwhip, which can slither as fast as you can run. But the prettiest is the Sonoran mountain kingsnake.

You might think a kingsnake would be easy to see, with its fire-bright bands of red and white outlined in black. But this scaly camouflage actually blends in very well with the dappled leaf litter.

Kingsnakes aren't poisonous, but they strike hard like a fist, and squeeze whatever they want to death—lizards, bats, woodrats; even rattlesnakes.

In the desert, if you don't have fangs, aren't quick or big, and can't fly, the only way to defend yourself is by hiding. This tiny red-spotted toad looks like she has a bad case of the chickenpox—but her reddish-orange warts help hide her on the desert rocks.

Kiss frogs all you want, but don't kiss toads. Like all of her kind, she has two lumps right behind the eyes called parotoid glands, which contain irritating chemicals to ooze out onto any would-be predator. It won't harm human skin, though; feel free to pick her up.

Water doesn't last long in the desert, so red-spotted toads have special patches on their undersides (flip them over to check). After it rains, these patches act like sponges to absorb water directly through their skin.

Enjoy this hummingbird with its dapper, green feathers—there are no hummingbirds in Europe, Africa, Asia, Australia, or (obviously) Antarctica.

These birds are *tiny*. The bee hummingbird of Cuba is the smallest bird in the world. It would take two of them to weigh as much as this page of paper. The so-called giant hummingbird is only the weight of a mouse.

Hummingbird hearts beat 1,200 times per minute—the best you can do is break 200 b.p.m when you're running hard.

Hummingbird wings can beat up to seventy times per second and propel the bird at 34 miles per hour. If you take their diminutive size into account, an Anna's hummingbird is the fastest vertebrate in the world, moving 385 body lengths each second. (A cheetah can "just" move eighteen body lengths per second.)

We are saying goodbye to deserts by heading out at night to find two of God's least attractive creatures. Bring along a black light—they can't hide from that.

First, look out for bark scorpions. They may be small and carry their babies on their backs, but a single sting will give you the worst 72-hour nausea of your life, if it doesn't kill you first. They also appear bright blue under the ultraviolet light, which helps with locating them.

Sun spiders, ironically, hate light. God made this little guy so that scientists don't know exactly how to classify it within the arachnids, since it's neither a scorpion nor a spider. It is amazing, though, with huge jaws that can be a third of its body length.

Some biologists argue that it has the strongest jaws of the animal kingdom for its size.

SRI LANKA

If you can begin to appreciate an Arizona sun spider going at full speed on its eight fleshy legs, you are ready to head abroad to Sri Lanka. The island sits in the sapphire sea south of India, and it's a place of arid lowlands, lush jungles, dense rainforests, and even high-elevation cloud forests. What seems normal to the people here looks exotic to our eyes, but once again we can see that the Great Artist seems to love the color green best.

Sri Lanka is home to almost five hundred species of birds, including blue magpies and serpent eagles and wild peacocks and hornbills and kingfishers and storks and egrets. But the national bird of Sri Lanka is a red junglefowl, more popularly known as...a wild chicken. These chickens are proof that, if you have the eyes to see, it's no wonder God said each new creature was good.

Dr. Wilson loves watching the determined and diligent weaver bird. Instead of building a typical cupped nest in a thick forking branch, each pair of these weavers chooses a single, swinging twig as a foundation for a new home. And then they begin to weave dangling basket nests, one of the most complicated bird constructions in all the world. Perhaps the wind in the thorn trees will rock their fledglings to sleep.

25

Smaller birds were harassing this crested serpent-eagle's crown of feathers, but she wasn't chasing them away...because she was focused on the ground.

Unfortunately, someone else beat her to the prize (which was a tasty land monitor). Now a changeable hawk-eagle has got the lizard in his talons and is fighting to subdue it. A land monitor is a formidable opponent, growing as long as child is tall and weighing up to twenty pounds (a hawk-eagle only weighs four). Monitors are armed with vicious claws, unrelenting jaws, and a powerful whipping tail.

This whipping, striking, ripping battle has lasted for an hour, and the monitor is weakening. Soon the exhausted hawk-eagle will have a belly full of lizard meat to take back to its single nestling—and all the struggle will be worth it.

In Sri Lanka, we see reminders of the Fall—like a warthog chewing away at the corpse of a wild water buffalo, waited on by crows, jackals, and a white-bellied sea eagle. There are only a few thousand wild water buffalo left on the planet.

At the same time, we continue to see glimpses of Eden—the elephant. Massive and ponderous, with long, dexterous noses to use as both straws for slurping and arms for carrying, elephants live as long as people. They are loyal to their friends and family, and they are unique among animals in their grief at death. They gather together and mourn the loss of one of their herd, performing burials with leaves and branches and even revisiting death sites years later.

Elephants have even been known to travel many miles to mourn the death of a human friend—somehow they can sense the loss, even at a distance. Wrinkled, bristly, and baggy, only God could make creatures so funny looking and yet so noble.

The Hanuman langur is a leaf-eater, named after a monkey-faced Hindu god. Usually langurs are too quick for large predators, but that won't stop this Sri Lankan leopard from trying for a baby monkey. Occasionally, she will catch one.

You wouldn't feel as sorry if you knew how langurs treat their own infants. They are as wickedly behaved as elephant seals. In a monkey troop, each infant has the same father, and if a new male tries to take over, he will try to kill the infants so he can replace them with his own babies.

When we study God's many, many words in nature, one of the first things you will notice is that His taste is often nothing like ours. Sure, we love His sunsets. We love swaying forests and ancient, sprawling trees. We love calm water reflecting the sky. We love bunny rabbits and harbor seals. But what about things like bats?

Flying foxes gather in city-sized colonies thousands strong. They sport black, four-foot wingspans with long finger-like claws, but are fluffy and orange in the center. Even though they can fly at three months old, mothers nurse their pups until five months. Full adulthood only comes around eighteen months.

Would Christians ever dare to proclaim their hatred of any part of God's Word? And yet we are often quick to stick up at our noses at God's living and breathing art made flesh around us.

God not only provides for His creatures, but He gives them the right tastes and appetites. For example, geckos relish termites, which is really convenient for us humans. Eat up, geckos! We'll take care of the bacon.

Birds are very good at figuring out how to prepare their food for themselves. This blue magpie has learned how to rub the defensive barbs off caterpillars diligently before dining.

Not all critters have lovable appetites. This land leech can grow to the size of a pinkie finger, armed with teeth at both ends. It can climb and grab and hold with those toothy head and tail suckers. Next time you're in Sri Lanka, it will hunt you by smelling your exhaled CO_2. It wants a little of your blood.

Here is a local snake doctor, Waidyarathna, with a deceptively venomous krait. For more than 120 years, this man's family has been at the forefront of the local battle between humans and serpents—not through destruction, but with cures. Long before scientists had even begun work on antivenins, this family had developed herbal remedies for the deadliest of bites. They still house any bite victim, rich or poor, for as long as it takes to cure (or bury) them. They also collect snakes, and will let you take a good look at them.

The Indian rock python is nonvenomous with a powerful bite, and it is a famous constrictor. Kaa from Rudyard Kipling's *Jungle Books* is an enormous Indian rock python, and the rock python is often used a model for picture-Bible artists painting the serpent in the Garden. Too bad they got stuck with this image. They don't tempt people to sin—they are just fond of your chickens.

Most venomous of all is the Russell's viper, a circle-splotched, triangle-headed lurker that kills thousands all over Asia and India every year. It isn't particularly aggressive, but it can hurl all five feet of its body length into the air when it strikes. Its venom can solidify a cup of human blood in seconds.

Last but far from least is the egg-adoring spectacled cobra. There's nothing adorable about a snake that weaves and hisses like a cougar as it watches you, its hood spotted with fake monster eyes.

All cobras are venomous, and the largest, the king cobra, can grow as long as a giraffe is tall. One bite from a king cobra delivers enough venom to kill an elephant. Its fangs are fixed like fishhooks, ready to deliver neurotoxins to stop your breathing muscles and cardiotoxins to stop your heart.

Christians who take the Bible seriously believe that a fundamental conflict exists between mankind and serpents (Gen. 3:15). Statistics argue the same

point—the World Health Organization claims that 100,000 people are killed by venomous snakes every year. But will this struggle continue forever?

Isaiah 11:8 says, "The nursing child shall play by the cobra's hole, and the weaned child shall put his hand in the viper's den." Either Isaiah is saying that the good news of Jesus's resurrection will triumph so completely that we *and* venomous serpents will both behave...or he's saying there will be cobras in heaven. Or both.

Until then, let's play, Cobra. We know your Creator, and we brought water balloons.